The CHILDREN'S BIBLE

101 Favorite Bible Stories

Sally Ann Wright and Carla Manea

CONTENTS
OLD TESTAMENT

CONTENTS
NEW TESTAMENT

THE OLD
TESTAMENT

IN THE BEGINNING

Genesis 1:1—2:3

In the beginning, before there was earth or sky, and before creatures of every kind lived on the earth, everything was dark.

Then God said, 'Let there be light!'

Light shone in the darkness, and God was so pleased that he went on to make the land, the sea and the sky. Then God filled the earth with plants and trees, fruit and flowers and arranged lights in the sky to separate the day and the night. The warm, bright sun gave light during the day and a silver moon and sparkly stars lit up the dark night sky.

God made his world beautiful. He filled the seas with colorful creatures—sharp and spiky, smooth and silvery—and filled the skies with the sound of singing songbirds, buzzing insects and delicate butterflies.

God made animals of every kind: spotted, striped and patterned, crawling, climbing, hopping and galloping.

God was pleased with all he had made. Yet… God wanted something else, people, a man and a woman, to be his friends, and to take care of the world he had made. God made Adam and Eve. Then he rested from the work of creation.

Genesis 3:1-6

God gave Adam and Eve a leafy garden to live in, watered by a stream. He told them they could eat anything that grew there, except the fruit from the tree in the middle of the garden.

Day by day, God talked to Adam and Eve. They were his friends and they were happy.

A snake also lived in the beautiful garden. The snake asked Eve about the fruit on the tree in the middle until it seemed larger and juicier and more delicious than the fruit from any other tree.

Eve picked the fruit and took a bite. Then she shared it with Adam.

THE BROKEN RULE

Genesis 3:7-23

As soon as they had tasted the fruit, Adam and Eve knew they had done something wrong. God had given them everything. He had asked them to obey just one rule—and they had broken it.

They looked at each other. They felt guilty. They felt ashamed. They had spoilt everything.

When God came to speak to them, Adam and Eve hid from him. Everything had changed. They knew they couldn't be his special friends any more.

Adam and Eve left the beautiful garden. God was very sad, but he knew that he would always be there when they needed him.

CAIN AND ABEL

Genesis 4:1-11

Adam and Eve had two sons. Cain, the older brother, grew up to work in the fields. Abel, the younger brother, looked after the sheep and goats.

Cain brought some of his grain to thank God for the good harvest. Abel chose his best lamb to thank God for all the new baby animals that had been born.

Cain was sure that God liked Abel's gift more than his own. It made him jealous. What happens when people are jealous of someone else?

Cain sulked. He could not stop thinking about his brother.
The more he thought, the angrier he became. God warned Cain to
be careful… but Cain started to imagine what it would be like if his
brother was not there at all.

One day Cain asked Abel to go for a walk—and then he
attacked his brother and killed him.

'Where is your brother?' God asked Cain.
'I don't know,' Cain lied. 'Is it my job to look after him?'
God knew that Cain had done a terrible thing. His beautiful world
was no longer such a good place to be.

NOAH BUILDS AN ARK

Genesis 6:9-22

As time passed, God saw that people hurt each other. They were selfish and greedy. They were only happy if they took what they wanted from others.

One man was different. Noah tried to be kind and looked after God's world.

God told Noah to build an ark—a huge boat—big enough to carry two each of all the creatures that lived on the earth. And Noah did. People laughed at him but Noah collected together lots of food—and then, two by two, birds and animals of every kind came to him.

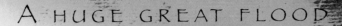

A HUGE GREAT FLOOD

Genesis 7:1-24

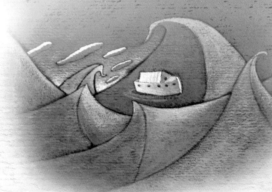

When Noah, his family and all the animals were safe inside the ark, it began to rain. Slowly, steadily, hour after hour, day after day, week after week, it rained. It rained until flood waters covered the earth and all the people who were cruel and greedy and had hurt each other were washed away.

Only Noah's ark floated above it all.

After forty day and forty nights, the rain stopped. The clouds drifted away and the sun shone. Slowly, steadily, hour after hour, day after day, week after week, the waters went down and the land dried out.

Genesis 8:1—9:17

After forty days, Noah opened a window and let out a raven. It did not return. Then Noah sent out a dove, but there was nowhere yet for it to rest its legs. Seven days later, Noah sent out the dove again. This time it returned with a fresh olive leaf in its beak.

Now the earth was clean and new and dry and the trees were producing leaves and flowers and fruit.

God told Noah to open the door of the ark—and all the animals
that had been kept safe there followed each other out on to the land
to start again.

Noah thanked God for keeping him and his family safe from the flood.
And God promised there would never be another flood like it.

Then a dazzling bright rainbow filled the sky as a sign of God's promise.

A MAN CALLED ABRAHAM

Genesis 12:1-5, 15:1-6

Abraham was, like Noah, a good man. God had plans to make him the first of a great nation of people.

God promised him a new land to live in and as many children as there was dust on the earth and stars in the sky.

Abraham trusted God. When God told him to leave his home and move to another place, Abraham took his wife, Sarah, his servants and their camels, sheep and goats, and went to the place that God told him would be his new home.

When they got there, they saw that it was just as beautiful as God had promised.

ISAAC IS BORN

Genesis 18:1-15; 21:1-7

Abraham and Sarah settled in the land of Canaan. They were happy.
There was just one thing worrying them. God had promised them
descendants—but how could that be when they didn't have any
children?

One day strangers came to Abraham's tents. Abraham knew how
to make visitors welcome. He made sure they had shade to sit in and
prepared a feast for them to eat.

'When we return this time next year—your wife will be holding
your son in her arms,' they told Abraham.

Then Abraham realized that God himself
had sent them. And God kept his
promise. Some time later, Sarah
gave birth to baby Isaac.

ABRAHAM'S FAMILY GROWS

Genesis 25:19-28

Isaac married Rebekah when he grew up. After some time, twin boys were born.

Esau, who became a skillful hunter, was his father's favorite. Rebekah loved Jacob best. He stayed with her and loved to cook.

One day Jacob was cooking a tasty stew.

'That smells wonderful!' said Esau. He had been out hunting and was very hungry. 'I'd do anything to eat some of that now!'

'You can have some,' said Jacob, 'if you will give me Father's blessing in return.'

Esau was the eldest son. One day he would receive the special blessing given to the son who was born first. But he gave it away for a bowl of stew.

JACOB TRICKS HIS FATHER

Genesis 27:1-41

When Isaac was old and almost blind, he asked to see his eldest son. 'Go and hunt for me,' he asked Esau. 'Then I can eat my favorite meal and bless you before I die.'

As soon as Esau had gone, Rebekah called Jacob. She gave him Esau's clothes to wear so Jacob smelled like his brother. She wrapped animal skins around his arms and neck so that he felt hairy like his brother. Then she cooked Isaac a tasty meal.

That day, Isaac blessed Jacob, thinking that he was his eldest son. Esau was so angry, he wanted to kill his brother!

JACOB'S DREAM

Genesis 27:1-44; 28:10-22

Rebekah was afraid for her son and told him to go and stay for a while with her brother Laban.

On the way, Jacob stopped to rest for the night. With a stone for his pillow, he fell asleep under the stars. And Jacob dreamed.

He dreamed that he saw a staircase leading from the earth to the sky above. Angels were climbing up and down the staircase and God himself was at the top.

'I am the God of your grandfather Abraham and your father Isaac,' said God. 'This land will one day be your land and I will take care of you.'

When Jacob woke up, he decided that the God of his dream would now be his God.

Jacob stayed with his Uncle Laban and worked for him. He married his cousin Rachel because he loved her; he married Leah because his uncle tricked him! And Jacob had a large family of twelve sons and a daughter.

JOSEPH, THE FAVORITE SON

Genesis 27:1-41

Jacob loved his son Joseph best of all. He gave him a special brightly colored coat as a present. But this made Joseph's brothers jealous. They wished Jacob loved them half as much.

Joseph made things worse. He had strange dreams about

sheaves of corn and stars in the sky… and the only possible meaning of his dreams was that one day Joseph thought that he would be greater than all his family—and his brothers would bow down before him.

Soon Joseph had made enemies of his older brothers. They began to think of ways to get rid of him.

One day, while the brothers were out taking care of their father's sheep, Jacob sent Joseph to see them.

The brothers realized this could be their chance. First they threw him down a well. There wasn't any water in it but Joseph was still down a deep dark hole—and he didn't think it was very funny.

Then they decided to sell Joseph to some traders who were passing. The brothers counted out the coins—and then dipped Joseph's beautiful coat in goat's blood.

When Jacob saw the coat, he thought his favorite son had been killed by a wild animal! Jacob thought he would never be happy again.

Meanwhile, Joseph could not understand what had happened to him. One day he was Jacob's favorite son and had everything he wanted; the next... he was mistreated and deserted by his brothers and his life would never be the same again.

It was a long, dusty journey to Egypt—and when he got there, he was sold as a slave to a man called Potiphar. Joseph decided to work hard and do his best and soon Potiphar trusted him with everything in his house.

God was taking good care of Joseph.

But Potiphar's wife liked Joseph a little too much. Joseph had to find ways to keep away from her all the time. Finally she told lies about Joseph to get him into trouble—and Joseph found that he was no longer a slave in the house of an important man—he was a prisoner in an Egyptian jail.

JOSEPH, THE PRISONER

Genesis 39:21-23; 40:1-23

Joseph decided to work hard and do his best and soon the jailer trusted him with everything in the prison.

Joseph spent long years there. But when Pharaoh became angry with his baker and cupbearer, Joseph saw a way out. Both men had strange dreams—and Jacob told them that his God could tell him what the dreams meant. It was good news for the cupbearer: Joseph said that soon he would be free to work for Pharaoh again. It was bad news for the baker: he would be executed!

When the cupbearer left the jail, he promised to tell Pharaoh that Joseph had done nothing wrong and should not be a prisoner at all… but once he was free, he forgot all about Joseph.

DREAMS COME TRUE

Genesis 41—47

Two years later it was Pharaoh's turn to have strange dreams.

'I know who can help you!' said the cupbearer, remembering Joseph at last.

Joseph was brought from the prison and as he listened, God made clear to him that they were a warning. First there would be seven years of good harvests with plenty for everyone to eat. But then there would be seven years of terrible famine. Someone should store the grain carefully so that no one need go hungry when the harvests failed.

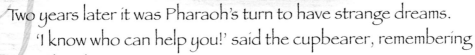

Pharaoh agreed. He gave Joseph the next most important job in the land to himself.

More dreams came true when Joseph's brothers came to Egypt hoping to buy food. They bowed down to the man who could help them—and found that he was their little brother! Jacob was overjoyed to find his son was still alive, and the whole family came to live in the land of Egypt.

MIRIAM AND THE PRINCESS

Exodus 1:1—2:10

The Israelites made Egypt their home for years after Joseph had died. God blessed them with many children and they grew to number many thousands of people.

So when a new king became ruler over Egypt, he was afraid of the large numbers of Israelites. First he made slaves from God's people and worked them hard. Then he made his soldiers take away all the baby boys who were born—and drown them in the River Nile.

When Jochebed gave birth to a beautiful baby boy, she hid him so that the soldiers would not find him. Then, as he grew a little

older, she wove a basket and made it waterproof. She placed her baby boy in the basket and hid him in the reeds by the river. Miriam, his big sister, watched from a distance to see what would happen.

Miriam watched as an Egyptian princess came to the river to bathe. When the princess saw the basket and found the little baby boy inside, she wanted to keep him.

'I will call you Moses,' she said.

Miriam asked the princess if she would like someone to take care of the baby for her—and so it was that Moses was cared for by his mother, under the protection of the princess.

THE BURNING BUSH

Exodus 3:1 – 4:17

One day, when Moses had grown into a young man, he saw an Egyptian slavedriver beating an Israelite. He was so angry that he killed the slavedriver! Moses tried to hide what he had done, but he was so afraid of being found out that he ran away into the desert.

Moses married a wife in Midian and made his home there. For many years he took care of his father-in-law's sheep until—God spoke to him from a bush which seemed to be burning in the desert.

'Go to the king of Egypt,' said God. 'Tell him to let my people go!'

Moses was afraid. He didn't want to go to the king. He was sure the king would not listen to him!

'Take your brother Aaron with you,' said God, 'and I will tell you what to say.'

PLAGUES IN EGYPT

Exodus 7:15—11:10

So Moses and Aaron went to see the king.

'God says, "Let my people go,"' they said. But instead the king told the slave drivers to make the Israelites work even harder.

Then God sent terrible plagues to make the king of Egypt change his mind. The River Nile became as red as blood and frogs invaded the land. There was a plague of biting gnats and a plague of buzzing flies. All the animals that worked on the land for the Egyptians became ill and died and the people were covered in painful sores. A terrible hailstorm destroyed the new crops and locusts ate anything that was left. Then darkness covered the land for three days.

After each plague, the king of Egypt agreed to let God's people go—but then he changed his mind.

ESCAPE FROM EGYPT

Exodus 12:31-38, 13:21—14:31

After nine plagues, God's people were still slaves in Egypt. God then told Moses that the tenth would be the most terrible of all the plagues. The people must get ready to leave Egypt—for soon they would be free.

Moses told everyone to mark their doorposts with lamb's blood and pack their bags. They must prepare and eat a meal of roast lamb with herbs and bread while wearing their shoes and cloaks.

That night, the angel of death passed over the homes of all God's people. But every first-born Egyptian male died—including the king's own son.

'Take your people and everything you own and go!' the king shouted at Moses.

There were hundreds of thousands of Israelites with many more thousands of sheep and goats. The Egyptians were so pleased to see them go that they also gave them silver and gold. God appeared as a pillar of cloud to lead them by day and as a pillar of fire by night.

But the people had not gone very far with their heavy loads when… the king changed his mind once more. He prepared his armies and his best chariots and chased after them.

Now the Israelites had the Red Sea in front of them and the Egyptian chariots behind them.

'God will prove today that he will take care of us,' said Moses, and he stretched out his staff.

God sent a strong wind to blow back the waters and the Israelites crossed safely to the other side. Then Moses stretched out his hand again. The waters returned just as the Egyptians started to follow. God's people were free.

TEN RULES FOR LIFE

Exodus 20:1-17

God's people wandered in the desert for a long time. When they were thirsty, God provided clean water for them to drink. When they were hungry, God provided quails and sweet honey cakes to eat.

God also gave Moses rules known as the Ten Commandments so his people could live together in peace.

'I am your God, who rescued you when you were slaves in Egypt. Don't worship anyone or anything else.

'Don't make something into a pretend god and worship that.

'Use my name when you pray to me but don't use it as a swear word.

'Keep one day a week special and rest from your work.

'Love your mother and father and respect them.

'Don't plot to kill anyone.

'Love your husband or wife and be faithful to them.

'Don't take something that belongs to someone else.

'Don't tell lies about other people.

'Don't be greedy and want things that other people have.'

RAHAB AND THE SPIES

Joshua 2:1-12

The Israelites lived in the desert for many years but after Moses died, God asked Joshua to take his people into Canaan.

First Joshua sent spies into Jericho, to see how easy it would be to get past the strong, high city walls. They went by night to the house of a woman called Rahab. But the King of Jericho found out that they were there.

'Bring out the spies, Rahab!' said the king's men. 'We know they are with you.'

Rahab hid the spies under the flax drying on her roof—and she sent the men away, telling them that the spies had left before the gates had shut.

'Why are you helping us?' asked the spies.

'Everyone knows that your God is the one true God,' said Rahab. 'Nothing can stop you. Be kind to my family when you come through Jericho and I will help you escape now.'

THE WALLS CAME TUMBLING DOWN

Joshua 2:21, 3:1-17, 6:1-23

Rahab let a rope down from her window. Then the spies climbed down the city wall. Rahab tied a red cord to mark where she lived.

When Joshua heard from the spies that the people of Jericho knew they could not fight the Israelites and win, he organized them to cross the River Jordan. Soon they would be ready to enter the city and then the promised land of Canaan.

The priests crossed the river first, carrying the special box in which they kept the ten commandments. The water stopped flowing straight away and the people crossed the River Jordan on dry land.

Then Joshua made the people march around the city walls behind the priests who blew loudly on their trumpets. For six days they marched and blew while the people of Jericho watched.

On the seventh day, they marched seven times around the city walls. Then when the priests blew on their trumpets, all the Israelites shouted… and the walls of Jericho came tumbling down.

The Israelites saw the red cord in the window of Rahab's house— and she and all her family were kept safe.

THE CANAANITES FIGHT BACK

Judges 4:1-23

God's people made their home in Canaan. But when Joshua died, they forgot to follow God's laws. They even forgot who God was.

It was only when the people who lived round about started to attack them that they asked God to help them once more.

Deborah was a prophet. So when God answered their prayers, she told Barak to trust God and lead the people into battle against Sisera, his many troops and chariots.

'I can't do it!' said Barak. 'At least—only if you will come with me.'

Deborah went with Barak—but she told him that God would give the victory not to him but to a woman.

Barak led the people and a fierce battle took place. All of Sisera's troops were killed that day. Sisera fled, exhausted and frightened, to a tent where a woman called Jael offered him a place to hide. When Sisera fell asleep, she killed him using a tent peg.

GOD'S SIGN TO GIDEON

Judges 6:1—7:23

There was peace in the land again—until once more God's people forgot how he had helped them. Then Midianites rode in on camels and stole all their crops—again and again—until God's people prayed to him for help.

God answered their prayers by sending Gideon to save his people. But Gideon was afraid. He asked God to give him a sign that he could trust him.

That night Gideon put out a woolen fleece on the ground and asked God to make it wet with dew while the ground stayed dry. God answered his prayer.

The next night Gideon put out the woolen fleece again and asked God to make the fleece dry while the ground was wet. God answered his prayer.

Gideon was still afraid—but now he trusted God to help him. He led a small army of only 300 soldiers to the Midianite camp by night—and drove the enemy away, just as God had promised.

SAMSON, THE STRONG MAN

Judges 13:24—16:30

Long after Gideon, the Philistines began to terrorize God's people. God sent Samson to help them.

Samson was unlike any other man. He wore his long hair in seven braids. He had enough strength to fight a grown lion with his bare hands. And he killed 1000 Philistines with the jawbone of a donkey.

The Philistines were afraid of Samson, and while he lived, God's people were safe.

Samson had a weakness. The Philistines did not know why he was so strong but they did know that he loved pretty women. They bribed Delilah to find out how they could overcome him.

Day after day Delilah teased him; she pleaded with him; she begged him, until finally he could take it no longer.

'Ok! I'll tell you,' he answered. 'God is my helper. If my hair is shaved off, I will become as weak as any man.'

So Delilah betrayed Samson. The Philistines shaved off his hair while he was sleeping and he was captured, blinded and thrown in prison.

Some time later, the Philistines had a great celebration. Thousands of people came to see how the great man had fallen. So Samson was brought from the prison and placed between the two great pillars. The Philistines laughed and jeered at him. And Samson prayed to God.

'Remember me, Lord. Please—give me back my strength just once more, so that I can destroy your enemies and die with them.'

Samson pushed on the pillars with all his strength—and they began to crumble. The walls came down, killing everyone inside.

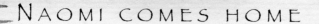

NAOMI COMES HOME

Ruth 1:1–22

Naomi and her husband had made their home in Moab when there was a famine in Bethlehem. Naomi's husband died there but her two sons married local girls. For a while they were happy. But some years later, Naomi's sons died too.

Naomi had lost everything. She had no husband and she had lost both her sons. She wanted to go home.

'Go back to your mothers,' she told her daughters-in-law. 'You have been kind to me but I am alone now. May God bless you both with new husbands and families of your own.'

Both girls cried and clung to Naomi and eventually Orpah went home. But Ruth would not leave Naomi.

'Don't make me go back,' Ruth said. 'Let me come with you wherever you go. I will never leave you. I will worship your God, and your home will be my home.'

So Naomi and Ruth went home together to Bethlehem, just as the barley was ready to be harvested there.

RUTH AND BOAZ

Ruth 1:2—4:16

Ruth went out into the fields to collect the barley left behind by the harvesters. She worked hard all day so that she and Naomi would have food to eat.

The man who owned the field was Boaz. He was a relative of Naomi's husband. Boaz noticed Ruth working and asked who she was.

'Make sure you come back here again,' he told her. 'I will make sure there is plenty left for you to pick up each day. You have been good to Naomi—and God will bless you for it.'

Naomi was very pleased that Boaz had noticed Ruth and pleased with all the grain she had been able to collect. After the harvest was finished Naomi helped Boaz to get to know Ruth better.

Naomi thought she had lost everything— but now she had a home in Bethlehem and enough to eat. She was looked after by her kind daughter-in-law and soon she was happy at the marriage of Ruth and Boaz. Later, she held her little grandson, Obed, in her arms. Naomi knew that God had blessed her.

THE BOY WHO LISTENED

1 Samuel 1:11, 20; 3:1-10

Hannah had been married for a long time but still she had no baby—and Hannah wanted a baby very much. Hannah prayed, and she promised God that if she could have a baby boy, he would serve him all his life.

God answered Hannah's prayer. She was very happy when baby Samuel was born, but when the time came, Hannah sent Samuel to Eli, the priest, so he could learn how to serve God.

One night, Samuel heard someone call his name. He went to Eli's room because he was sure Eli must be calling him. But Eli was asleep.

'Go back to bed,' said Eli.

But later, Samuel heard someone call his name again. He went to Eli.

'Go back to bed,' said Eli. 'I didn't call you.'

When Samuel went to Eli a third time, Eli realized that the person who was calling him was God.

This time, when Samuel heard the voice, he answered, 'Speak to me, Lord. I am listening.'

Samuel listened when God spoke. He grew up to help God's people obey him.

THE FIRST KING

I Samuel 8:6—10:7; 15:1-23

Samuel led the people for a long time. But when he grew old, they came to him.

'You won't be able to lead us forever,' they said. 'We want a king. We want to be like all the other nations around us.'

Samuel told them that God was their king. But they wouldn't listen. So God told Samuel to give them what they asked for, and anoint Saul as first king of Israel.

When Samuel went to meet Saul, he was searching for his father's donkeys.

'Don't worry about the donkeys,' Samuel greeted him. 'They are safe and I will take you to them. But God has something more important for you to do!'

Saul was amazed—but he let Samuel anoint him as king.

At first Saul listened to God and did exactly what he told him to do. But when he saw how the people loved him, he forgot that it was because God had helped him. He began to do things his own way.

'Be careful, Saul,' warned Samuel. 'Reject God's ways now, and soon you will find that God rejects you as king.'

THE LAST SON

1 Samuel 16:1—10:7; 15:1-23

Samuel was unhappy at all that Saul did, but God had plans to make things right. He had already chosen someone to follow Saul.

'Go to Jesse's house in Bethlehem. Trust me. He has a son who will be the next king of Israel.'

So Samuel went to Bethlehem and invited Jesse and his sons to a feast. Jesse introduced his first son to Samuel. He was tall and handsome.

'Surely this is the man God has chosen,' Samuel thought.

'You see what the man looks like,' said God, 'but I see what's inside him. This is not the man I have chosen.'

Jesse introduced six more sons to Samuel. All were tall and handsome, but God had chosen none of them.

'Have you any other sons?' Samuel asked.

'Only David, my youngest,' Jesse replied. 'He is taking care of the sheep.'

As soon as David was brought to the feast, God spoke to Samuel.

'This is the one who will be king. Anoint him.'

THE SHEPHERD'S SONG

Psalm 23

David would one day be the king of Israel—but for now, he was protecting his father's sheep from lions, bears and wolves.

When he wasn't being a shepherd, David played the harp and made up songs.

'The Lord is my shepherd,' sang David. 'He makes sure I have everything I need. He leads me to places where I will be safe; he protects me from all kinds of danger. I will never be afraid because God is always with me; he takes good care of me.'

One of King Saul's men knew that David played the harp. Saul was often moody and bad tempered now. Perhaps David's harp would soothe him.

So David came to play for the king. His music did soothe him and Saul liked having David there.

DAVID FIGHTS A GIANT

1 Samuel 17:1-50

One day, when David was in Saul's camp, he saw a big man marching up and down and shouting in a big booming voice. Goliath, the Philistine champion, was covered top to toe in armor and carried some fierce looking weapons.

What was he shouting?

'Is there a man in the king's army?' the giant shouted. 'Is anyone brave enough to stand against me and fight?'

David was angry that Goliath was making fun of God when he made fun of God's people. If no one else would fight, then he would!

King Saul tried to dress David in his own armor. He put his helmet on his head. But the armor was too heavy; the helmet was too big. David took off the armor.

'God has saved me from the lion's paw before now,' David told Saul. 'I think he will help me now.'

Then David picked up five smooth pebbles from the river bed
and went out to face the giant. Goliath was angry. Were the Israelites
making fun of him to send a boy with a stone in his hand?

David put a stone in his sling and aimed it at Goliath—hitting
him dead center on his forehead, the only place not covered by his
helmet. The giant fell down dead.

A roar went up from Saul's army!
David was their hero. God had taken
care of him again.

SOLOMON'S GIFT FROM GOD

1 Kings 2:1-4

Saul saw that God had blessed David—and he was jealous. But after years of fighting, Saul died and David became king. For many years there was peace in the land of Israel.

David had a son called Solomon. When he lay dying, he wanted Solomon to be king after him.

'Make sure you listen to God,' David advised him. 'Follow his commandments and you will be a good king.'

One night, Solomon dreamed. He dreamed that God asked him to name any gift he wanted—and God promised to give it to him.

'What can I ask for that I don't already have,' Solomon answered. 'You have given me so much. Just make me wise so I can be a good king, and I will be happy.'

God was so pleased with Solomon's answer that he gave him wisdom, wealth and power. And all the people loved Solomon.

A VERY WISE KING

1 Kings 3:1-28

One day there was the noise of people arguing in Solomon's court. Two women came, asking the king to judge between them.

'Each of us had a baby boy,' said one. 'In the night, her baby died. She stole my son and put her dead baby in my bed!'

'No,' shouted the other. 'The dead baby is hers!'

'Stop!' said Solomon. 'Cut the baby in half. Then you will both be happy.'

'No!' said the real mother. 'Do not kill him. Give her the baby.'

Solomon smiled. He knew the real mother would not let her baby die. She took her son away that day, happy with his judgment.

Everyone heard of Solomon's wisdom and saw that God had blessed him. He built a beautiful temple so that people could worship God and he tried to follow God's ways. He was a wise king and a good king.

No clouds in the sky

1 Kings 17:1-6

Elijah looked up at the clear blue sky. There was not a cloud anywhere—just like yesterday and the day before and the day before that. The river beds were dry and cracked. The earth was parched.

Elijah drank from the clear stream still bubbling beside him. He was waiting for the big, black ravens who brought him breakfast each morning and supper before the sun went down.

King Ahab had refused to listen to Elijah's warnings from God.

'Stop worshipping these false gods,' Elijah had told him. Worship the true and living God of Abraham, Isaac and Jacob—or God will send no more rain.'

King Ahab had been very angry. Elijah had not stayed long enough to find out just how angry.

No more rain fell after that. Day after hot, dusty day passed. Weeks and months passed in the same way. But God had shown Elijah the bubbling stream. God had instructed the ravens to bring him food. God was taking good care of Elijah.

Some time would pass before the stream dried up. Then, Elijah knew, God would show him what to do next.

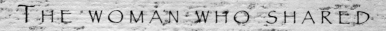

THE WOMAN WHO SHARED

1 Kings 17:7-16

'Go to Zarephath,' God told Elijah, when the water no longer flowed in the stream. 'You will find there a widow. She will share her food with you.'

Elijah found the woman gathering sticks to make the last meal for herself and her son before they died of hunger. She had only one drop of oil and a handful of flour left. But she kneaded the flour and she baked the bread and she shared it with Elijah.

When the woman looked again, there was flour enough in the jar and oil enough in the jug to make another meal.

For as long as the woman shared what she had with Elijah, God made sure that she and her son would not be hungry.

WICKED KING AHAB

1 Kings 18:4-15

While Elijah had been away, Obadiah had been given the job of finding food and water for King Ahab and the people in the palace.

Ahab had murdered many of God's prophets, but Obadiah risked his own life to hide a hundred of them in two caves. He brought them something to eat and drink each day.

Now suddenly, he met Elijah on the road.

'Is it really you?' he asked.

'Yes,' said Elijah. 'You can go and tell the king that I am here.'

'But he will kill me!' said Obadiah. 'Don't you know how angry he is? Don't you know that he has been looking for you for three years? You will disappear again as soon as I give him the news and he will think it is all my fault!'

'Tell him I am here,' said Elijah. 'It is time I spoke to him.'

JONAH RUNS AWAY

Jonah 1:1—2:9

God spoke to his prophet Jonah one day.

'Go to Nineveh, where the people are doing terrible things. Tell them I want them to stop.'

Jonah heard what God had said—but he didn't want to go to Nineveh! Instead he found a ship that was sailing in the other direction, paid his fare, made himself comfortable and fell asleep.

Soon a great storm blew up and waves lashed on to the deck. The sailors threw their cargo overboard but still they were afraid they would drown.

'Wake up, Jonah!' they called to him. 'Pray to your God to save us!'

Jonah knew the storm was his fault.

'I worship the God who made land and sea,' he said. 'Throw me into the sea and you will be safe.'

Jonah fell down, down into the cold, choppy waves and called out to God to save him. And God sent a huge fish to swallow him whole.

Almost immediately the wind dropped and the sea became calm.

Jonah stayed in the body of the fish for three days and three nights and, while he was there, he prayed.

'You are a great God,' Jonah prayed. 'You have power to give life and power to take it away. You answered me when I needed help and you gave me back my life.'

63

GOD FORGIVES

Jonah 3:1-10

God heard Jonah's prayer. He caused the huge fish to spit Jonah on to the beach. Jonah dusted himself down. When he heard God's message a second time, Jonah went to Nineveh.

For three days Jonah went through the city. He warned the people that God was unhappy. He told them they must stop doing bad things.

Then—to Jonah's horror, he saw that they were listening to him. He saw that they were sorry. He saw that they were ready to change and stop doing bad things. They even stopped eating and drinking, so that God would know they meant it.

God was happy that Jonah had delivered the message—and he forgave the people of Nineveh.

JONAH, THE GRUMPY PROPHET

Jonah 4:1-11

'I knew this would happen, God,' Jonah prayed. 'I knew that you were kind and loving. I knew you would forgive the wicked people of Nineveh even though they deserve every bad thing that you could do to them. This is why I didn't want to come and bring them your message!'

Jonah left the city. He sat under a shelter in the sun and he sulked. God made a vine to grow up over the shelter to give Jonah shade—and Jonah was happy. But the next day a worm ate the vine and it died. Jonah was hot and miserable.

'Well,' said God. 'You are upset that the vine has died though you didn't make it and you didn't look after it. Can you see how much more upset I would be if the people of Nineveh died? I did make them; I do look after them. Every one of the people I have made matter to me—wherever they come from.'

God's plans for Jeremiah

Jeremiah 1:5-9, 52:1-3; 2 Chronicles 36:11-21

Jeremiah was a young man when God spoke to him first.

'I had plans for you before you were born, Jeremiah,' said God. 'I want you to speak for me and I will tell you what to say. Don't be afraid—I will help you.'

No one wanted to listen to Jeremiah. No one wanted to follow God's commandments.

'Listen to God,' pleaded Jeremiah. 'God is warning you. The Babylonians are coming! They will destroy Jerusalem and steal from God's temple. People will die. Others will be taken prisoner.'

King after king ignored Jeremiah. King Zedekiah even threw him in a pit!

Finally, Jeremiah saw God's words come true. The Babylonians broke down the walls of Jerusalem and plundered Solomon's beautiful temple. They murdered the king's sons and blinded King Zedekiah. They took him and many others away in chains.

'Don't be afraid, Jeremiah. I will help you,' said God.

God's plan for Jeremiah meant staying behind in Jerusalem. He took care of the people who were left there.

THE FIERY FURNACE

Daniel 3:1-30

King Nebuchadnezzar believed he was a powerful man. He had a huge golden statue built so that it could be seen for miles around. Then he gave orders that whenever the music played, everyone should worship the statue. Anyone who did not would be thrown into a fiery furnace.

Everyone was afraid of the king. Everyone worshipped the golden statue—except Shadrach, Meshach and Abednego.

'Can it be true?' the king roared at them. 'Worship my statue now or you will go into the fiery furnace. No one can save you then!'

'God may save us, or he may not,' they answered. 'But we will not worship anyone but him.'

So Nebuchadnezzar had the men thrown into the furnace.

Inside the king was amazed to see not three, but four men walking about. He ordered them to come out and saw that they were alive and well—and didn't even smell of smoke!

'Your God sent an angel to save you,' he said. 'There is no other God like yours!'

THE MADNESS OF THE KING

Daniel 4:1-37

King Nebuchadnezzar had another bad dream. When Daniel heard it, he knew the king would not want to hear its meaning.

'Tell me, Daniel. Don't be afraid,' said the king.

'I wish your dream was about someone else,' said Daniel. 'But everything you saw will happen to you. Your dream means that it is time for your power to come to an end. You will live outside like a wild animal and you will eat grass like cattle. So please, be sorry now for your sins. Do what is right and good. Be kind where before you were cruel. Then maybe you can stop this happening.'

But the king carried on as before until his dream came true. His hair grew long and straggly, his nails became like claws and he lived outside like an animal. Then one day he realized how great God is, and how small man is. Then King Nebuchadnezzar was healed of his madness.

THE WRITING ON THE WALL

Daniel 5:1-30

Nebuchadnezzar's son became king after him. Belshazzar held a party and called for the golden goblets from the temple in Jerusalem to be brought out and filled with wine.

As he drank, he saw words appear on the wall, written by the fingers of a human hand. Belshazzar went white with fear. He called for the wise men but no one understood the words or what had happened.

Then someone remembered Daniel. Belshazzar offered him expensive gifts if he could explain the meaning of the words.

Daniel would not accept his gifts, but he told the king that God was about to bring his kingdom to an end and it would be divided between the Medes and the Persians. And that night Darius the Mede took over his kingdom and Belshazzar was killed.

EZRA GOES HOME

Ezra 7:6-28

King Artaxerxes saw that Babylon was full of Israelites who had been brought from Jerusalem. He decided that it was time for them to go home.

Ezra had studied God's laws. He took as many families as would go with him and they made their home again in Jerusalem. Artaxerxes told them to take back gold and silver that had been stolen so they could rebuild God's temple there.

'Lord, we have ignored your kindness, we have disobeyed your laws and we have been slaves because of it,' prayed Ezra. 'But you have been good to us. Thank you for the chance to start again.'

After many years in exile, God blessed his people once more.

BROKEN WALLS

Nehemiah 2:1-18, 6:15, 8:5-10

Nehemiah was still in Babylon, cupbearer to King Artaxerxes. One day, he had news from Jerusalem that the people there were in danger because the walls were still broken down.

When the king asked him why he looked so sad, Nehemiah told him.

'I want to go home,' he said. 'I want to rebuild the walls and gates of my city.'

Artaxerxes not only let Nehemiah go, he told Nehemiah to get the timber for the rebuilding from his own forests. God was on Nehemiah's side.

Nehemiah helped the people in Jerusalem to repair the city walls and build new gates in only fifty-two days. Then Ezra read out God's commandments to the people. They cried over the things they had done wrong. They thanked God for bringing them home.

THE NEW
TESTAMENT

THE ANGEL GABRIEL

Luke 1:26-38

Mary was going to be married. The village carpenter, a good man named Joseph, would be her husband. But some time before their wedding, God sent the angel Gabriel to her home in Nazareth in Galilee.

'God has chosen you, Mary,' said the angel. 'You are very special. You will give birth to a son, and you will call him Jesus.'

'But I am not even married yet,' said Mary. 'How can this happen?'

'Nothing is too hard for God,' the angel told her. 'This child will be called God's son.'

Mary loved God. She was happy to accept God's plan for her.

THE JOURNEY TO BETHLEHEM

Luke 2:1-5

Mary told her cousin Elizabeth about the angel's visit. Elizabeth was pregnant too, and when she saw Mary, the baby moved inside her, happy at the wonderful news!

Mary and Joseph prepared for the arrival of her baby son. But just as she was nearing the time for the baby's birth, the Roman emperor, Caesar Augustus, ordered everyone to return to their home town to be counted.

So Joseph took Mary to Bethlehem, because his family was descended from King David himself. It was there that Mary's baby son was born. They called him Jesus.

TESTS FOR JESUS

Matthew 4:1-11

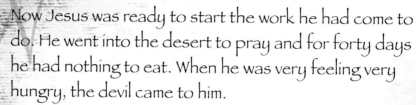

Now Jesus was ready to start the work he had come to do. He went into the desert to pray and for forty days he had nothing to eat. When he was very feeling very hungry, the devil came to him.

'You could make these stones into bread to eat—if you are God's son,' said the devil teasingly.

'It is written that man needs more than bread to live,' Jesus replied.

The devil then took Jesus to the highest part of the temple in Jerusalem. 'Throw yourself down! It is written that God's angels will catch you,' he said.

'It is also written that we should not put God to the test,' replied Jesus.

The devil then took Jesus to a high mountain. 'Worship me, and all this is yours.'

'It is written that we should worship only the Lord God,' replied Jesus.

Then the devil left Jesus alone.

JESUS CHOOSES SPECIAL FRIENDS

Luke 5:8-11

Jesus saw the fishermen fixing their nets by Lake Galilee. He asked Peter to take him out on the water.

'Let down your nets and see what you can catch,' Jesus suggested.

'Master, we have just got back from a bad night's fishing—we caught nothing!'

But Peter and Andrew threw the nets over the side, just the same. Suddenly there were fat fish everywhere, glistening in the sunshine. James and John came to help them.

'Follow me—and catch men for God instead of fish,' said Jesus.

Peter, Andrew, James and John followed Jesus from that day on. Later they were joined by Philip, Bartholomew, Matthew, Thomas, another James, Simon and two men called Judas.

THE STORM ON THE LAKE

Mark 4:35-41

Jesus didn't just heal people—he taught them about how much God loved them. And although their teachers had told them many things about God before, somehow all the rules they had to learn had got in the way. Jesus was reminding them about what really mattered— about loving God and caring for other people.

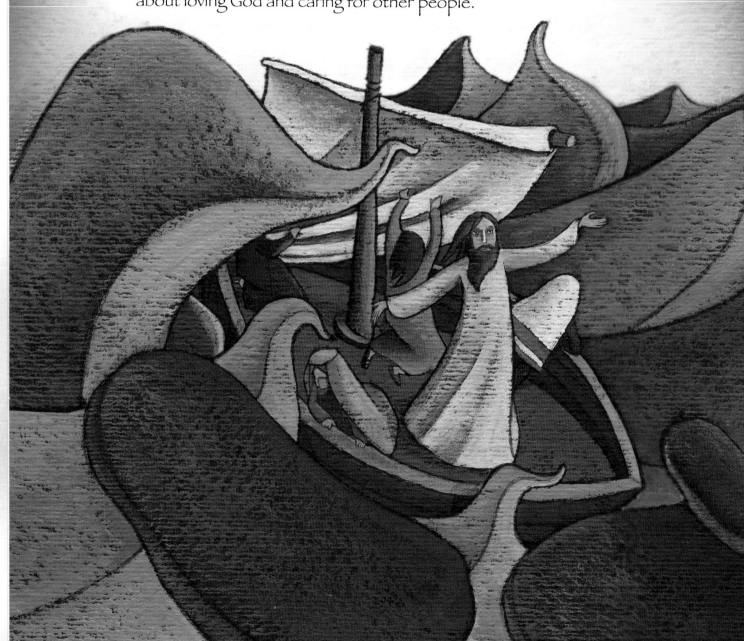

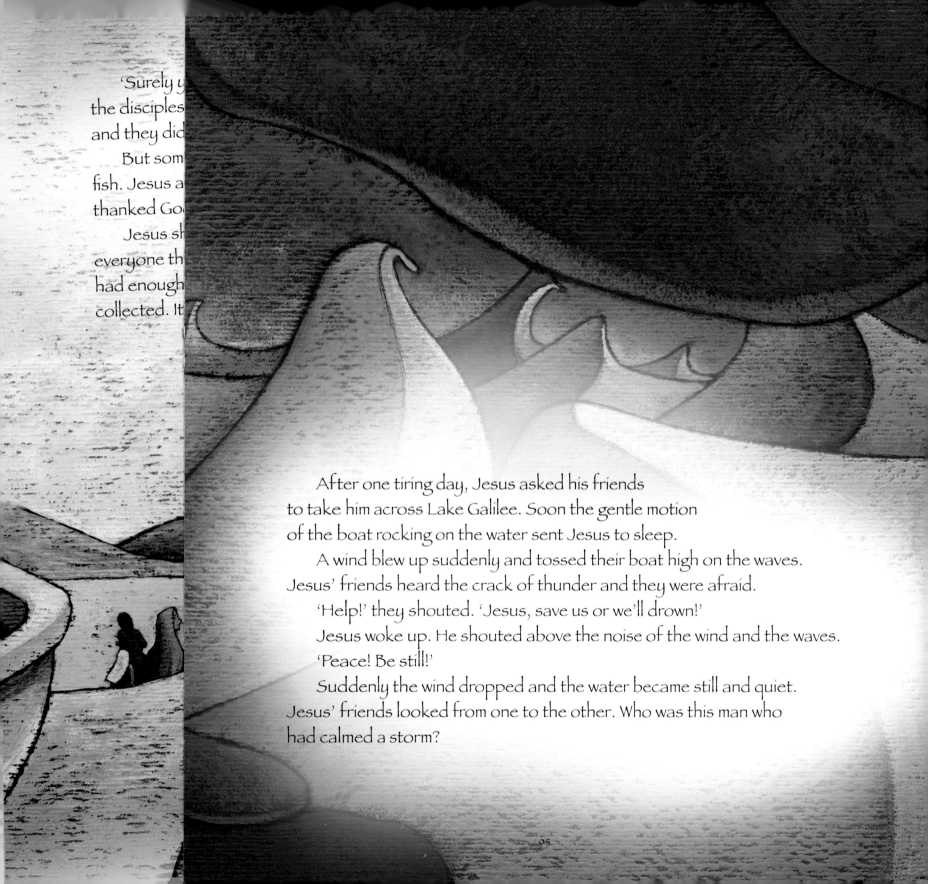

'Surely y[...]
the disciples[...]
and they did[...]
But som[...]
fish. Jesus a[...]
thanked Go[...]
Jesus sh[...]
everyone th[...]
had enough[...]
collected. It[...]

After one tiring day, Jesus asked his friends
to take him across Lake Galilee. Soon the gentle motion
of the boat rocking on the water sent Jesus to sleep.

A wind blew up suddenly and tossed their boat high on the waves.
Jesus' friends heard the crack of thunder and they were afraid.

'Help!' they shouted. 'Jesus, save us or we'll drown!'

Jesus woke up. He shouted above the noise of the wind and the waves.

'Peace! Be still!'

Suddenly the wind dropped and the water became still and quiet.
Jesus' friends looked from one to the other. Who was this man who
had calmed a storm?

Still the c
all hopin
Jesu
a lonely
them, hi
to eat.

FRIENDS IN BETHANY

John 11:1-45

Lazarus was very ill. Mary and Martha sent a message to tell Jesus. He often stayed at their house. They knew he would want to know.

When Jesus heard the news, he knew that a great miracle was going to take place. He stayed where he was a little longer so he could finish what he had come to do there. Then he made his way to Bethany.

Lazarus had already died by the time he reached the village. He had been in the tomb for four days.

'This wouldn't have happened if you'd been here,' Martha told him sadly. 'But I know it's not too late.'

'Do you really believe I can help him, Martha? Do you know that anyone who believes in me will live for ever?'

'Yes,' she replied. 'I have always known that you are God's Son.'

Mary joined them and all the people who had come to support the sisters came too. They took Jesus to the tomb where they had buried Lazarus. Soon Jesus was weeping with the sisters.

Then Jesus turned to the tomb and asked them to move the stone door. Martha was afraid but Jesus asked God to help them. Then he called to Lazarus to come out of the tomb.

Everyone stared, amazed, as Lazarus walked out, still wrapped in strips of cloth.

'Help him out of those graveclothes,' said Jesus. He will be OK now.'

'Surely you can find food for everyone here?' asked Jesus. But the disciples shook their heads. There were over 5000 people there and they did not have enough money.

But someone had offered them five small rolls and two little fish. Jesus asked everyone to sit down, then he took the food and thanked God for it.

Jesus shared the food with his friends and they handed it to everyone there. Somehow as people shared and ate, everyone had enough to eat and there were even twelve baskets of leftovers collected. It was a miracle!

JESUS HEALS A DEAF MAN

Mark 7:31-37

Another time a man was brought to Jesus who could not hear and who could hardly speak. Could Jesus help this deaf man to hear the sound of the birds singing? Could Jesus heal him so that he could listen to his family talking around him—and even talk back to them?

Jesus took the man away from the anxious crowd. He touched the man's ears and his tongue.

Be opened!' he said aloud.

Then suddenly the man could hear Jesus and all the sounds around him—and he could speak! His friends and family were so excited they could not stop talking about it.

'Jesus is amazing,' they said. 'He can even make the deaf hear and the mute speak!'

The story of the good Samaritan

Luke 10:25-37

One day a man asked Jesus about God's commandments.

'I know I must love God with all my heart, mind and strength, and I must love my neighbor as I love myself,' he said. 'But tell me—who is my neighbor?'

Jesus told a story to answer his question.

'A man was attacked while walking from Jerusalem to Jericho. He was left dying by the side of the road.

'A priest saw the injured man, but walked on by. A Levite saw him, but walked on by. Then a Samaritan saw him. He stopped and bandaged the man's wounds, sat him on his donkey, and took him to an inn. He paid the innkeeper to take care of him until he came back.

'Now, which of the three men was a neighbor to the wounded man?'

'The one who stopped and helped him?' The man replied.

'Then you know the answer. This is what you must do also.'

THE STORY OF THE LOST SHEEP

Luke 15:1–7

Jesus also told a story about a sheep that got lost.

'Once there was a shepherd who had a hundred sheep. He knew the names of every one. They knew his voice and he knew the different sounds they made.

'One day when he counted his sheep, he found that there were only ninety-nine. One of them was lost! The shepherd made sure that the others were safe and then he went looking for the missing sheep.

'He searched for hours until, finally, he heard the sound of bleating. He rescued the little sheep and carried him home. Then he threw a party because he was so happy to have found his sheep!

'God is like that shepherd,' said Jesus. 'He cares about every one of the people he has made, especially the one who is all alone and needs his help.'

The story of the loving father

Luke 15:11-31

Jesus once told a story about a father who loved both his sons—
even when the youngest decided to leave home.

'The boy made lots of friends who helped him spend his money,'
said Jesus. 'He had a wonderful time. But when all the money was
gone, his friends left him too. He got the only job he could, looking
after smelly pigs. He wished he were home with his family.

'"I will go home to my father," he thought. "I will tell him I am
sorry."

'As the boy came near to his father's farm, now dirty and dressed
in rags, he saw his father watching, waiting.

'The boy tried to say how sorry he was that he had left home.
But his father's arms were already wrapped around him. He was
crying with joy to see his son again.

'"You are home and that's all that matters,"
said his father. "We must celebrate!"

'God watches and waits
for us to say sorry just like
that father. He is always ready
to forgive us.'

THE MAN WHO SAID THANK YOU

Luke 17:11-19

As Jesus came near to a village, he saw a small crowd of men standing at a distance. Some covered their faces. Others huddled together and shuffled on bandaged feet. They seemed to be waiting for him.

'Help us, Jesus,' they called out.

Jesus knew they had leprosy, a horrible skin disease that people were afraid of catching. He counted ten men.

'Go to your homes,' he said them. 'Don't be afraid—I have healed you.'

The men were overjoyed. Not only was their skin whole again—it meant they could live among their families; they were no longer outcasts. They quickly made their way to their homes.

One of the ten, a Samaritan, came to Jesus.

'Praise God!' he said. 'Thank you for what you have done!'

Jesus smiled at the Samaritan, but he looked into the distance at the other nine men.

FRIENDS IN BETHANY

John 11:1-45

Lazarus was very ill. Mary and Martha sent a message to tell Jesus. He often stayed at their house. They knew he would want to know.

When Jesus heard the news, he knew that a great miracle was going to take place. He stayed where he was a little longer so he could finish what he had come to do there. Then he made his way to Bethany.

Lazarus had already died by the time he reached the village. He had been in the tomb for four days.

'This wouldn't have happened if you'd been here,' Martha told him sadly. 'But I know it's not too late.'

'Do you really believe I can help him, Martha? Do you know that anyone who believes in me will live for ever?'

'Yes,' she replied. 'I have always known that you are God's Son.'

Mary joined them and all the people who had come to support the sisters came too. They took Jesus to the tomb where they had buried Lazarus. Soon Jesus was weeping with the sisters.

Then Jesus turned to the tomb and asked them to move the stone door. Martha was afraid but Jesus asked God to help them. Then he called to Lazarus to come out of the tomb.

Everyone stared, amazed, as Lazarus walked out, still wrapped in strips of cloth.

'Help him out of those graveclothes,' said Jesus. He will be OK now.'

Many of the people who were there realized that Jesus had brought a man back from the dead. It was a miracle. Jesus must be God's Son.

JESUS BLESSES CHILDREN

Mark 10:13-16

'Look! There's Jesus!'

Mothers carried their babies. Small children ran to see Jesus. Everyone knew that he was special. Everyone wanted to be with him.

Sometimes the disciples tried to protect Jesus from too many people.

'Let them come,' Jesus said. 'Don't try to stop them. They don't ask complicated questions. They know whom they can trust. And they trust me. If only some of the grown ups could do that too!'

Then Jesus lifted the children into his arms and blessed each of them.

THE MAN WHO COULD NOT SEE

Mark 10:46-52

Bartimaeus heard a crowd of people coming along the street. He turned toward the sound.

'Who is it?' he shouted. 'Who's coming?'

'Sshh, old man,' someone answered. 'It's Jesus!'

Bartimaeus knew who Jesus was. He had even heard that Jesus had healed people like him who were blind. If he could see, then he wouldn't have to sit by the roadside begging any more.

'Jesus! Help me!' Bartimaeus shouted.

Jesus was surrounded by people. But he heard Bartimaeus calling to him. 'Bring him here,' he said.

Bartimaeus threw off his cloak and walked toward the sound of Jesus' voice.

'What can I do for you?' Jesus asked.

'I want to see!' said Bartimaeus.

'Go,' smiled Jesus. 'I know you believe I can heal you.'

Bartimaeus smiled back, then he laughed out loud. He could see Jesus. He could see! He joined with all the others following Jesus and went with him down the road.

THE MAN WHO CLIMBED A TREE

Luke 19:1-10

112

Zacchaeus lived in Jericho, just like Bartimaeus. But unlike Bartimaeus, he hadn't spent his life in ragged clothing, begging for money. Zacchaeus was rich—very rich. He earned his money collecting taxes for the Romans.

People hated the Romans. They also hated anyone who helped them, especially when those people took more than they should and lived a life of luxury paid for by ordinary people.

When Zacchaeus heard that Jesus was in Jericho, he wanted to see him too. But he was not very tall and could not see over the heads of the people. No one would let him through.

So Zacchaeus climbed into the branches of a fig tree. Now he could see Jesus coming toward him. He had a better view than anyone!

'Hello, Zacchaeus!' said Jesus. 'I thought I might come to your house today.'

The people around Jesus frowned and shook their heads. Why was Zacchaeus up a tree? And why would Jesus want to go the house of a cheat?

'Please, come this way,' said Zacchaeus, who was very excited.

Zacchaeus was a changed man after he had been with Jesus.

'I want to give away half of all I have,' said Zacchaeus. 'I want to help the poor. And if anyone thinks I have cheated them—well, I will pay it all back—I'll pay them four times as much!'

'Today you have become God's friend,' Jesus said.

JESUS IN THE TEMPLE

Matthew 21:12-16

When Jesus went to the temple to pray, he was upset by what he saw there.

Voices were raised. There was bustle and confusion. It was more like a marketplace than a place of prayer… and just like the marketplace, Jesus saw that moneychangers were cheating people.

'Out!' Jesus shouted. 'This should be a place of prayer, but you have made it into a den of robbers!'

Then people came to Jesus as they always did, asking him to heal them. Children ran about him praising God for the wonderful things he did. But the priests and teachers were not so happy. They began to plot to get rid of him.

John 13:1-15; Matthew 26:26-29

Jesus was with his twelve friends, preparing to eat one last meal with them. He knew that Judas was ready to betray him. He knew that only a few hours would pass before he was arrested.

What could Jesus tell them? Jesus picked up a towel and a bowl of water. He started to wash their feet, the job usually performed by a servant.

'What are you doing?' asked Peter, shocked.

'I am showing you how to look after each other,' Jesus explained. 'This is how you can show other people how much you love me. Love each other.'

When they sat down to eat, Jesus shared some bread with all of his friends. He offered them a cup of wine to drink.

'This bread is my body, broken for you. This wine is my blood, spilled for you. Eat and drink and remember this when you eat together again.'

Praying in the Garden

Mark 14:32-50

Judas had crept out of the room while Jesus was talking. He went to the chief priests and told them where Jesus would be that night. He left with thirty silver coins jingling in a money bag.

After they had eaten and sung a song of praise to God together, Jesus wanted to pray. He went with his friends to a quiet place among the olive trees called Gethsemane.

He asked Peter, James and John to walk a little further with him and watch for a while. Jesus knew that he was in danger. But his friends were sleepy.

Then Jesus asked God to help him face the difficult hours ahead. But when he went back to his friends, they had all fallen asleep. Jesus woke them and asked them again to watch while he prayed. Again they fell asleep.

A little while later, Jesus saw that it was too late. In the moonlight they saw Judas coming toward them, leading a gang of armed men.

Judas met Jesus and greeted him in the usual way with a kiss. But this was the signal he had agreed with the men he had brought with him. They stepped forward and arrested Jesus. His friends were so afraid, they ran away and left him to be marched away.

THE ROOSTER THAT CROWED AT DAWN

Mark 14:66-72

Peter had been pacing about all night. When Jesus had been arrested he had followed in the shadows to see what would happen. Now he alone was waiting in the courtyard of the High Priest's house, hoping for news of Jesus.

'Aren't you a friend of the man they brought in earlier?' a girl asked Peter.

'Not me!' Peter moved away.

The girl was sure she was right but again Peter denied it.

When another group of people accused him, Peter became quite angry.

Then the rooster crowed. It was dawn. And Peter remembered something Jesus had said: 'Before the rooster crows you will say three times that you don't even know me.'

THE CROWN OF THORNS

John 18:28—19:16

Jesus was moved from place to place that night. Finally Pontius Pilate, the Roman governor, questioned him.

Pilate was troubled. He knew the Jewish leaders wanted Jesus out of the way, but he could find no crime to charge him with. He did not want to be guilty of the death of an innocent man.

Pilate went to the angry crowd outside and asked them what he should do with Jesus.

'I can release one prisoner as it is Passover time,' he said. 'Shall I release Jesus of Nazareth—your King? Or do you want the murderer, Barabbas?'

There were people in the crowd who had been bribed by the Jewish leaders.

'Barabbas!' they shouted. 'We want Barabbas!'

'Then what shall I do with Jesus?' he asked again.

'Crucify him!' came the answer. 'Crucify him!'

JESUS DIES ON A CROSS

John 19:17-42

It was Friday morning. Pilate washed his hands of the decision to have Jesus crucified. He turned away. Then Jesus was beaten. Weak and bleeding, he was made to carry a huge piece of wood along the streets to a place outside the city walls.

Jesus was put on the cross between two criminals to die.

Pilate arranged for a sign to be put over him saying: 'Jesus of Nazareth, the King of the Jews.' It was written in three languages, Hebrew, Latin and Greek, so that as many people as possible could read what it said.

The priests saw the sign and objected.

'Surely it should say, "He said, I am King of the Jews."?'

But Pilate would not change the sign. He knew who Jesus was.

Jesus' mother was there, weeping. John, his friend, waited with Mary and many of his other friends. After many hours, the sky turned black, and Jesus shouted, 'It is finished!'

Jesus was dead.

It was almost the beginning of the Sabbath day which began when the sun went down. The religious leaders wanted the bodies moved before then so the soldiers broke the legs of the two thieves to make them die more quickly. Because Jesus was already dead, a soldier put a sword in his side.

Then Joseph, a man from Aramathea, asked for permission to take Jesus down from the cross. He and a secret believer, Nicodemus, carried his body to a tomb in a nearby garden. They rolled a huge stone door across the entrance to close it.

The Sabbath, the day of rest, had begun.

MARY WEEPS IN THE GARDEN

John 20:1-18

Some of Jesus' friends went very early on Sunday morning to the garden with spices. But when they reached the tomb, the stone had been rolled away from the entrance: there was no body there.

Mary Magdalene ran to get Peter and John. The men went to find out what had happened and saw that everything Mary had said was true. But then they returned to the city, leaving her weeping in the garden.

'Why are you crying?' a voice asked her. Mary saw angels through her tears! 'Jesus is not here—he is no longer dead, but alive!'

Then suddenly Mary heard another voice—one she knew very well. It was Jesus!

'Yes, it's me,' Jesus told her. 'I am really here. Go and tell the others.'

Mary could hardly wait to see the disciples. 'Jesus is alive!' she told them in a rush. 'I have seen him with my own eyes!'

JESUS IS ALIVE!

John 20:24-29

First Mary had seen Jesus, then ten of the disciples. But Thomas had not been there. Thomas couldn't be sure.

Then Jesus came to the locked room where all eleven disciples were together.

'Come, Thomas,' said Jesus. 'Touch my hands. See for yourself that I am real and that I am alive.'

Thomas got down on his knees. Now he knew that Jesus was real.

'My Lord and my God!' he said.

FISH FOR BREAKFAST

John 21:1-14

Jesus was alive. He had risen from the dead. His friends had seen him. Hundreds of people who had known him while he was with them every day had seen him.

Some days Jesus came and talked with them. On other days they waited but he did not come.

'Let's go fishing,' Peter said to his friends one evening. So together, seven of the men went out on the boat. They fished all night, but by sunrise they had still caught nothing.

'What have you caught?' shouted a man standing on the shore.

'Nothing!' they replied.

'Throw your nets on the right hand side of the boat,' the man shouted back.

The men had nothing to lose. They threw the net one last time—and felt it pull against them as it filled with silvery fish! Peter looked again at the man. He knew it could only be Jesus.

Peter jumped over the side, leaving his friends to bring in the boat. He joined Jesus who was cooking fish and warming bread over a fire and soon they were all eating breakfast together.

'Do you love me, Peter?' Jesus asked his friend. 'Do you love me enough to do something very important for me? Will you take care of the others, teach them and lead them when I have gone?'

'You know I love you, Lord,' Peter replied. 'You know I will do anything you want me to.'

It was enough. Peter knew that Jesus had forgiven him and trusted him again.

THE HOLY SPIRIT

Acts 1:9-11, 2:1-12

Jesus told his friends that he would be going back to his Father in heaven—but he promised that he would send his Holy Spirit to be with them. It would be as if he was always with them.

The Holy Spirit came to them when they were in Jerusalem, celebrating the festival of Pentecost. They heard a sound like the wind. They saw flames of fire. Then they knew that they had the power to do anything.

'Tell God you are sorry for all the bad things you've done,' Peter told a huge crowd. 'Trust Jesus. He welcomes anyone who wants to be God's friend.'

The people listened. Over 3,000 people became friends of Jesus that day. They became known as Christians. They learned to look after each other as Jesus had told them. They shared everything they owned.

THE MAN AT THE GATE

Acts 3:1-10

At the gate of the temple a man was begging. He was brought there every day because he couldn't walk. He hoped that someone would give him money as they went to pray.

'Do you have any coins?' he asked Peter and John one afternoon. The men looked at him.

'We don't have any money to give, but we can give you something better. Jesus has given us power to help you walk. Stand up!'

The man stood and walked. He was so happy that he couldn't stop telling everyone what had happened to him.

'God is great! Look at me! I can walk!'

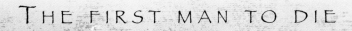

Stephen was one of seven men chosen to look after everyone who was in need. Stephen taught people about the things Jesus had said and done. He could heal people as Peter had done. People loved him.

The religious leaders were worried. Once they had been in charge; now people listened to the Christians instead. They had made sure that Jesus was crucified. Now they had to stop his followers.

They marched Stephen outside the city. He was not afraid. But he was killed for trying to teach people about Jesus.

A young man named Saul watched him die. Saul loved God. But he hated the Christians. He would not rest until all of them were in prison.

PAUL MEETS JESUS

Acts 9:1-25

Saul went to Damascus. But on the way, he was blinded by a light that shone all around him.

'Saul, Saul,' said a voice, 'why are you attacking me?'

'Who are you?' Saul asked.

'I am Jesus,' he replied. 'When you hurt my friends, you hurt me too. But I have something important for you to do. Go into the city and you will find out what it is.'

Saul had been traveling with friends—they had heard the voice that came from nowhere too. They led him into Damascus where, a few days later, a man called Ananias came to see him.

'Jesus has told me all about you. He has sent me to help you see again,' Ananias told Saul.

Then Saul's life was completely changed. He received the Holy Spirit and was baptized. No one could stop him from telling other people about Jesus!

But when the religious leaders heard what had happened, they planned to kill him. His friends had to help him escape in a basket from a window in the city walls.

THE MAN IN THE CHARIOT

Acts 8:26-39

The new Christians all found that their lives had changed.

Philip was told by an angel exactly where to go so that he could help a man from Ethiopia.

When Philip went to Gaza, he saw the man sitting in a chariot. He was reading words from the prophet Isaiah.

While he was wondering what to do next, the Holy Spirit told Philip to go nearer. Philip offered to help the man.

'Tell me, this seems to be a prophecy about someone who has died. Can you explain it?'

Philip got into the chariot and began to tell the man all about Jesus and how he had been crucified. He told him that God had raised him from the dead by a miracle—and now all his friends had received power to live as new people.

'Look,' said the Ethiopian, 'here's a stream of water. Will you baptize me? I want to be a Christian too.'

The chariot stopped and Philip baptized the man in the water.

Then the Holy Spirit found somewhere else for Philip to be, and other people to help. The two men did not meet again. But both knew that Jesus had special things for them to do.

The soldier who loved God

Acts 10:1-7

Cornelius was captain of the Italian Guard and was stationed in Caesarea. He loved God and was a good man. He prayed often and was always ready to help anyone who needed it.

But he was very surprised when he had a vision one afternoon. An angel—so real he could almost touch him—came and spoke to him.

'God has seen how kind you are and he has heard your prayers, Cornelius. He wants you to meet Peter, who is staying with Simon in Joppa, down by the sea.'

Cornelius told his servants and one of his soldiers what had happened. Then he sent them to fetch Peter from Joppa.

PETER'S VISION

Acts 10:9-23

While the men were traveling to Joppa, God was speaking to Peter in a vision.

He was on the balcony of the house when he saw a huge blanket, filled with every kind of creature, being lowered to the ground.

'Peter, you are hungry,' said a voice. 'Have something to eat.'

'But not all these foods are allowed for us to eat,' said Peter. 'I can't do it.'

'God has made the foods good,' said the voice. 'You can eat them, Peter.'

Peter woke from the trance to hear someone knocking at the door.

'Captain Cornelius has invited you to his house,' the men told Peter. 'An angel told him that you wanted to talk to him.'

When Peter went to see Cornelius the next day, he realized what his vision meant. God had told him that he welcomed people from every nation. Cornelius and his friends were Romans not Jews—but God had blessed them. Peter told them all about Jesus—and they were baptized into God's family.

PEOPLE PRAY FOR PETER

Acts 12:6-19

It was not safe to be a Christian. But people who knew Jesus could not stop telling others about him.

Then James, one of the first disciples, was executed. After this, Peter was put in prison. King Herod planned a public trial, hoping to stop other people from becoming Christians. He made sure Peter was heavily guarded and chained between two soldiers.

Peter's friends were worried about what would happen to him. They got together and prayed that God would help him.

That night, God sent an angel to the prison cell.

'Quickly!' he said. 'Wake up, put on your shoes and wrap your cloak around you.'

Peter watched with amazement as the chains fell off his wrists and doors opened and closed! He left the soldiers sleeping and followed the angel into the street. He went straight to his friends' house and banged on the door.

Rhoda, the servant girl, went to see who was there.

'It's Peter! He's at the door!' she told them. Rhoda was so excited, she had left him standing outside! But at first no one would believe her. Peter banged again on the door until they let him in.

God had answered their prayers! Peter was safe and with them again. Then he told his friends the story of the miracle that had brought him there.

But King Herod could not understand how Peter had escaped. He was very angry.

An earthquake in the prison

Acts 16:1-36

Meanwhile Paul had started traveling from country to country so that everyone could know Jesus in the way he did.

Paul healed people as well as teaching them about Jesus. Sometimes he was welcomed and churches were started because of him. At other times he was chased out of the city. Once people attacked him and left him for dead.

Then in Philippi, Paul and Silas were beaten and put in the stocks inside a prison. Even this did not stop them singing hymns to God and praying. Suddenly an earthquake rocked the foundations! The doors flew open and their chains were loosened. But Paul and Silas did not escape. Instead they told the jailor all about Jesus and the man—and his whole family—became Christians and were baptized.

The next day, Paul and Silas were released.

138

THE STORM AND THE SHIPWRECK

Acts 27:1-44

Paul spent his life being arrested and freed again and spent years inside a prison cell. But he used every chance he had to tell other people about Jesus. Finally he was sent to Rome to stand trial there.

While he was on the ship, they ran into a terrible storm. The ship was badly battered and they had to throw the cargo overboard. Weeks passed without food or water and the sailors tried to escape leaving all the passengers to die. But an angel told Paul that God would keep everyone safe and they would get to Rome.

The ship was wrecked off the coast of Malta. Some of the passengers swam to the shore while others drifted, clinging to the wreckage. Not one life was lost.

Travels in Malta and Rome

Paul and the other 275 people on board the ship spent the next three months on the island of Malta, where Paul healed many people on the island who were ill. When it was safe to travel again, they were given a ship and food for the journey.

Then in Rome, Paul was given somewhere to live with a soldier to guard him. He invited the Jewish people who lived there to see him and he shared with them all he knew about Jesus. Some of them became Christians.

Then he welcomed anyone who would listen to come to see him. Paul spent the next two years telling people about what had happened to Jesus and writing to the new churches, helping them to live the way God wanted them to.

He reminded everyone that they could show people how much they loved God by taking care of each other and treating other people well.

The disciples had done what Jesus asked them to—going wherever they were welcome to tell others about him. The Christian church began with them and spread all over the world.

ANNO DOMINI

First edition 2011

Copyright © 2011 Anno Domini Publishing
www.ad-publishing.com
Text copyright © 2011 Sally Ann Wright
Illustrations copyright © 2011 Carla Manea

Editorial Director: Annette Reynolds
Art Director: Gerald Rogers
Pre-production Manager: Krystyna Hewitt
Production Manager: John Laister

US and Canadian distribution
Book Depot
67 Front Street North
Thorold, Ontario, L2V 1X3
Canada
www.bookcloseouts.com

Printed and bound in Singapore